Soil types

A field identification guide

By Stephen Trudgill

FSC
BRINGING
ENVIRONMENTAL
UNDERSTANDING TO ALL

© FSC 1989

ISBN 978 1 85153 196 7

Occasional Publication 196

CONTENTS

ACKNOWLEDGEMENTS

I am grateful to, firstly, those teachers who have fiercely, and justly, demanded that academics present soils in an interesting and simple way, rather than showing off how much they know and saying how complicated it all is; secondly, to those soil scientists who have equally fiercely, and justly, been critical of simple approaches which do not remain faithful to precise definitions of established soil types and, thirdly, to those who have helped in the attempt to find a balance between these two. I am especially grateful to the three anonymous referees of a preliminary draft; Tim Harrod and Steve Staines of the Soil Survey of England and Wales and Field Studies Council staff, both ecologists and geographers, especially David Job, Rob Lucas, Tim Mitcham, Keith Chell, Tony Thomas, Paul Croft, Nigel Coles and Liz Cole.

INTRODUCTION

This key has been developed for use in the field throughout Britain. Particular attention has been given to those soils found in semi-natural sites as they are the ones most often available for study. The guide is presented at two levels:

1. Introductory, allowing the beginner to study and identify the major soil types in the field;

2. More advanced, enabling the more experienced student to place a soil within a particular subdivision of soil types.

Soils can be extremely variable over space, and many intermediate forms exist which do not correspond with textbook types. In order to tackle these variations and intermediates, the following section provides description of fundamental soil processes. Once these have been understood, the main groups of soil types become easier to distinguish. Diagnostic features are described; these relate to soil development processes and can be compared with soil sections in the field to classify the soil without too much concern for other detail. The more detailed, specialist, information is included in Key 2. This is an adaptation of the soil descriptions used by Avery (1980) which can be referred to if greater detail is required. Please note that Soil Survey publications refer to *soil series*. These are groups of similar soils developed on similar parent material shown on a map and named after local types. They are not used here.

Teachers who are new to the field identification of soils are recommended to read Appendix 1 (p. 26). This may help when first planning the exercise.

SOIL DEVELOPMENT AND DIAGNOSTIC HORIZONS

Definitions and identification features

A soil is defined as the upper surface-layer of the earth, including loose mineral, dead organic and/or mixed mineral-organic material. Solid rock is excluded, as is living organic material. A true soil has distinct well-developed horizontal layers or *horizons* which are more organic at the surface, more mineral (and with a somewhat altered organic content below), grading into bedrock, sediment or other parent material underneath. However, there exist many thin (skeletal) soils which do not conform to this description.

The soil horizons can be viewed in a vertical section called the *soil profile* and form the main diagnostic features used for soil identification. In particular, soil colour is an important feature, as are the distributions and types of organic and mineral matter.

Horizons are keyed out in the Soil Horizons Key, p. 10, and are discussed in detail below.

Soil formation

Soil is formed when mineral matter reacts with the organisms, air and water present at the surface of the earth. The effects of these interactions – past and present – can be seen in the soil profile. Three processes are particularly important.

1. Interactions with organisms and their products

Organic matter (chiefly leaf litter but also including twigs, branches, faeces etc.) is derived from organisms living on, and in, the soil. If conditions are suitable, this detritus will be utilised by a variety of soil organisms ranging from earthworms to microscopic bacteria and fungi. The products resulting from this decomposition will be mixed with the mineral matter in the soil. Some species of earthworm are particularly important in this mixing process, ingesting plant and mineral material at the surface and depositing the mixed mineral-organic matter lower down. Such mixing imparts a dark colour to the topsoil because the organic matter is dominantly brown in colour (e.g. Plate 1). The decomposition pathways are illustrated in Fig. 1. Although this shows two distinct pathways, there will be intermediate stages between them (e.g. Plate 4). The two extremes may result either in a separate, deep organic horizon, termed an *O horizon,* or in a mixed mineral-organic horizon, termed an *A horizon* (e.g. Plates 1 and 3). Thus, if either of these horizons can be recognized in a soil profile, the soil development processes may be deduced. The horizons may be diagnostic when identifying soil types in Key 1.

Leaf litter gradually decomposes on the soil surface giving rise to a litter layer on top ('L' horizon), a decomposition or fermentation layer immediately below ('F' horizon) and a humus layer ('H' horizon) underneath, where plant remains are no longer recognisable. These, in themselves, are not diagnostic of soil types but where the H horizon extends well downwards it becomes an 'O' horizon. When the organic matter is mixed with the mineral matter below, it becomes an 'A' horizon.

Plate 1. A brown earth, developed on glacial till, Holderness, Humberside. Note the lack of distinct horizonation. The thin organic matter under the turf mat is well incorporated into a crumb structure 'A' horizon which is slightly darker (because of organic matter incorporation) than the prismatic structured 'B' horizon below into which it merges gradually. Key: No podzolic horizons, no gleying, no thick organic surface accumulation, therefore is Brown Earth in Key 1. In Key 2, this soil keys out: 2.4 – 1, 4, 5, 13, 15, 26, 30: Typical Brown Earth.

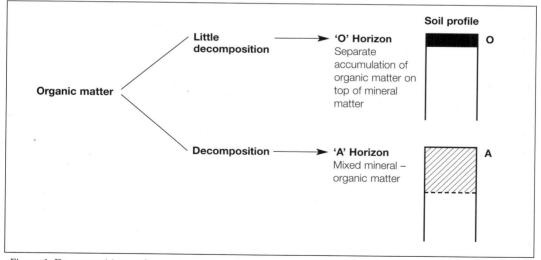

Figure 1. Decomposition pathways in soil formation. Two extremes are shown, but examples will be found of intermediate stages.

Under certain conditions the decomposer organisms cannot flourish – in areas where it is too cold, too wet or too acidic – and the organic material at the soil's surface will remain more-or-less intact.

Plate 2. Brown Calcareous earth on till over Magnesian Limestone, Whitwell Wood, S. Yorkshire. As in Plate 1 but under woodland. The organic matter is thicker than in Plate 1, but not deep enough to qualify as an 'O' horizon. Simple key: Brown Calcareous Earth. Presence of limestone in profile keys out via 2.4 – 1, 4, 5, 6, 10, 12: Typical Brown Calcareous Earth. Mapped by Soil Survey as Aberford Series: Typical Brown Calcareous Earth.

2. Interactions with air

Below the surface – topsoil – horizons there will be a predominantly mineral horizon, with very little organic matter present. This horizon is usually altered in some way by weathering and is termed the *B horizon*. One of the weathering processes is *oxidation*. This is the reaction of a mineral with oxygen derived from the air – either through direct contact with air in the soil pores or with oxygen dissolved in mobile soil water. The most noticeable form of oxidation involves iron. Iron in the oxidised state is red or red-brown in colour, i.e. rust coloured; this is ferric iron (= *Iron III*) which is trivalent (Fe^{3+}). Oxidation involves the loss of a negatively charged electron, a process which can also be induced by low acidity (for further reading, see Trudgill, 1983, pp. 72-73). The reverse process is one of *reduction* where iron is reduced to the ferrous form (= *Iron II*) by the gain of a negative electron, thus becoming divalent, (Fe^{2+}). Reduced iron is more soluble than oxidised iron and may be transported through the soil, often under conditions of high acidity (as discussed in Section 3 below). Reduced iron compounds are grey or bluey-grey in colour. Therefore, soils through which oxygen permeates

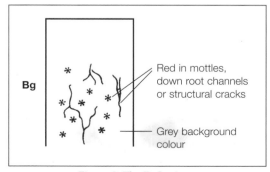

Figure 2. The Bg horizon.

Plate 3. Brown soil with gleying beneath. Simple key: Brown Earth. Keying depends on dominance of gleying; if strongly mottled, gleying puts it in Group II and is a Stagnogley; if weak, as in this case, becomes a Brown earth and keys to Gleyic Brown Earth via 2.4 – 1, 4, 5, 13, 15, 26, 27, 29.

Plate 4. Podzol, millstone grit soil, Pennines west of Sheffield, with organic matter above, Ea and iron rich layer below. Simple key: Podzol. Presence of iron layer below puts it in Group I, Podzols. Keys via 2.1 – 1, 2, 5, 6: Ferric Podzol. Thick organic matter could make it appear to be Humus-Iron Pan podzol, but would need mottling in Ea to key out as such.

(freely draining, open, porous soils) tend to be reddish brown (e.g. Plate 3). Less permeable soils (e.g. heavy clays and water-logged soils) are often grey (e.g. Plate 7), although some local oxidation may occur where air/water can permeate, giving rise to reddish mottling (e.g. down structural cracks or root channels; e.g. Plate 8). B horizons which are predominantly grey and/or red mottled are called *gley horizons* (e.g. Plate 8) and termed *Bg horizons*. Thus, such horizons, illustrated in Fig. 2, can again be used to interpret soil processes and to identify soil types, as shown in Key 1, p. 12.

3. Interactions with water

The products of weathering and decomposition can be transported down the profile in moving water – a process generally known as *leaching*. Technically, this term is used only to denote the processes where material is washed down the soil profile in simple solution. In addition, organic acids, produced in the soil surface horizons, can mobilise other compounds by a process known as *chelation*. These substances are not in true solution but are incorporated within the chemical structure of the organic compounds. Many compounds, especially of iron and aluminium, are more mobile when chelated than when they are in simple solution. In addition, as mentioned in Section 2 above, ferrous iron is

Plate 5. Podzol on sands, New Forest,
Hampshire, with Ea, Bh, Bs. Simple key: Podzol.
Bh and Bs put it in Podzol Group, I; keys via
2.1 – 1, 2, 5, 6, Bh > 2.5 cm: Humo-Ferric Podzol.

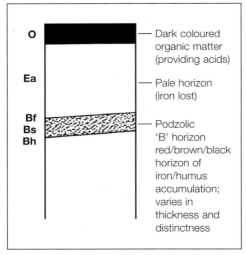

O	Dark coloured organic matter (providing acids)
Ea	Pale horizon (iron lost)
Bf Bs Bh	Podzolic 'B' horizon red/brown/black horizon of iron/humus accumulation; varies in thickness and distinctness

Figure 3. Podzolisation and the soil profile.

more mobile than ferric iron, and the former is often the form found under acid conditions. The downwashing of organic compounds and iron salts is termed *podzolisation*. Indications of podzolisation are thus: (a) surface accumulations of organic matter (often dark blackish, raw, acid humus) which can provide organic acids; (b) a paler horizon below, from which the iron has been removed, and (c) an accumulation of reddish brown iron and/or blackish humus downwashed into the B horizon (Fig. 3) (e.g. Plates 4 and 5).

The paler horizon from which the iron has been removed is an *eluvial* horizon (one from which material has been washed), and is given the notation *E*; a pale ash-like E horizon is termed the *Ea horizon*. *Podzolic B horizons* are accumulations of material (iron salts and humus) of varied thickness, distinctness and scale (Fig. 3; Plates 4 and 5). They can occur individually in a profile or may be found together (e.g. a Bs under a Bh or Bf). They can be differentiated as follows:

Bf – reddish/brownish accumulation of ferric iron, often hard as an 'iron pan', a few millimetres to a few centimetres thick (e.g. Plate 4).

Bs – an accumulation of sesquioxides (oxides with a ratio of 1:1.5 oxygen, i.e. Fe_2O_3 and Al_2O_3), more diffuse and extensive than a Bf, often with oxidation *in situ*, a reddish or reddish brown colour (e.g. Plate 4).

Bh – dark brown/blackish horizon of downwashed humus (decomposing organic matter) (e.g. Plate 5).

These horizons indicate that podzolisation has taken place and, again, can be used to identify soil types in Key 1, p. 12, even if cultivation or other disturbance has obscured the upper Ea and organic horizons.

Soils which have poor drainage and are waterlogged are often given the prefix *Stagno-*, indicating stagnant water conditions.

Plate 6. Chalk soil, Chiltern Hills (road cut for M40). Simple key: Rendzina. Keying depends on the thickness of the organic matter. If it is thin (< 10 cm), lacks a podzolic B horizon, gleying and a thick organic matter put it in Group IV. Keys via 21.5 – 1, 4, 5, 6, (calcareous) 10, 12 (Typical Brown Calcareous Earth). If the organic matter is thicker (> 10 cm, including chalk fragments), keys to Group III, Organic Soils and keys via 1, 5 (over bedrock), 10, 11 (Rendzinas), 15,17, and then Humic Rendzina if humose or Brown Rendzina (18, 19) if brownish. In this case, Humic Rendzinas are present, with deeper pockets of Brown Calcareous Earths. This particular area is mapped by the Soil Survey as the Icknield series, which is classified as a Humic Rendzina.

Summary

The colour of soil is important. Many soils are *brown* or *reddish brown*. Why? There are two reasons:

1. Dark, brown-coloured organic matter has been decomposed and mixed with the mineral matter (mostly by soil organisms such as earthworms).

2. Any iron present in such soils is in the oxidised state (ferric iron = iron III) which is red-brown in colour.

Additional features also provide a basis for identification of other soil processes:

3. Grey colour or mottled red and grey (indicating that the iron is not oxidised, or is not oxidised throughout, i.e. a reduced soil with gleyed horizons)

4. Organic matter accumulations on the surface (indicating a lack of decomposition).

5. Reddish brown/blackish horizons lower down in the profile (indicating downwashing of iron and/or humus under podzolisation).

Plate 7. Gleyed soil on alluvial clay, Forth Valley lowlands, Scotland. Simple key: Gley. Grey colour with some mottling put it in Group II. Keys via 2.2 – 1, 2, 3, 4, 5, 6, 10, 15: Alluvial Gley Soil.

These processes and features are not necessarily mutually exclusive and may be combined. However, they can be used as a basis for differentiation of the major soil types in Key 1, p. 12.

Further details on soil formation can be found in Courtney & Trudgill (1984).

Diagnostic horizons discussed above and used in Key 1

1. O – thick (10 cm) organic matter.
2. A – mixed mineral-organic matter (e.g. Plates 1 and 3).
3.* Bg – grey horizon, usually with red mottles (e.g. Plate 8).
4.* Ea – pale, bleached horizon below organic matter and above 5-7 (see below) (e.g. Plates 4 and 5).
5. Bf – iron pan (podzolic B horizon) (e.g. Plate 4).
6. Bs – diffuse reddish layer (podzolic B horizon) (e.g. Plate 4).
7. Bh – dark blackish organic matter (podzolic B horizon) (e.g. Plate 5).

***Important:** Both 3 and 4 can be pale, grey coloured but Ea occurs in combination with Bf/Bs/Bh. Information on the last three horizons – the podzolic B horizons – is given in Fig. 4.

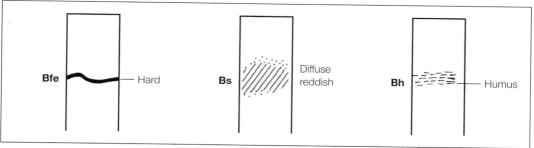

Figure 4. Podzolic B horizons.

A key to soil horizons is presented below. Use this key first to identify the horizon(s) before proceeding to the soil in Key 1, which recognises soil types through the presence or absence of particular horizons.

HOW TO USE THE KEYS

Having dug a pit down to the bedrock or other parent material, identification of the different horizontal layers can be attempted. The layers are distinguished by changes, especially of colour, and their extent should be marked by inserting sticks (or stones) at the boundaries where change occurs.

Starting at the top, and working downwards, the depth of each layer (from the top surface) should be measured downwards (so layer 1 might be 0-2 cm; layer 2, 2-2.5 cm; layer 3, 5-10 cm, etc.). Each layer should be described fully: is it organic humus, with/without mineral matter; is it brown, red or grey; is there any mottling; is it hard, or stony, and so on?

Plate 8. Gleyed soil in the New Forest. Simple key: Gley. As above,but higher elevation leads to 211-24, 25 (humose topsoil): Stagnohumic Gley Soil.

Appendix 2 gives details of how to recognise some additional soil characteristics (not all of which are needed for identification).

Enter the observations on the booking form, in the 'Descriptions' column Appendix 3 (p. 30), and subsequently use the Key to Soil Horizons to identify the layer, noting this on the right hand side of the booking form.

Lastly, Soil Key 1, The *Simplified Key to the Major Soil Types* (p. 12), or Soil Key 2, *The Detailed Soils Key* (p. 15), can be used to identify the soil type.

Fig. 5 provides a tabular summary of the characteristics of the major soil groups.

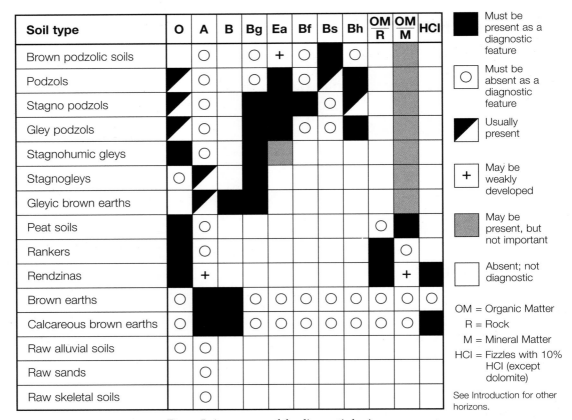

Figure 5. A summary of the diagnostic horizons.

KEY TO SOIL HORIZONS

H1 Surface horizons H2

-    Sub-surface horizons H5

W2 Organic (leaves, humus) H3

-    Not dominantly organic, mixed mineral-organic .... **A Horizon**

H3 Organic, more than 10 cm thick .... **O Horizon**

-    Organic, less than 10 cm thick over mineral soil or rock H4

H4 Read three alternatives

- Plant remains recognisable (leaves and stems) .... **L Horizon**

- Plant remains partly recognisable, partly decomposed .... **F Horizon**

- Plant remains decomposed; leaves and stems not recognisable, humus ...... **H Horizon**

H5 Grey (may have red mottles), may be very pale H6

- Not grey, usually brown/reddish/blackish H8

H6 Grey – mottled, wet soils, often clays, gleying .... **Bg Horizon**

- Grey – not mottled, or if so only sparsely. Below an organic horizon and above a brown/red/blackish layer. Eluvial horizons H7

H7 Mottled or very strongly blue grey .... **Eag Horizon**

- Not mottled: may be pale, bleached .... **Ea Horizon**

H8 Upper part of profile, mixed mineral-organic .... **A Horizon**

- Lower part of profile, B Horizons W9

H9 Distinctive features of iron pan, red/reddish/red-brown/blackish layers – podzolic B Horizons .... H 11

- Brown, lacking distinctive podzolic features .... H 11

H10 Read three alternatives

- Podzolic B – thin iron pan .... **Bf Horizon**

- Podzolic B – diffuse reddish .... **Bs Horizon**

- Podzolic B – blackish/dark brown, humus rich .... **Bh Horizon**

H11 Mottled, gleyed B .... **Bg Horizon**

- Not mottled .... **B Horizon**

Key 1. Simplified keys to the major soil types

This key covers the approximate groupings of the *main* soil types only. More precise details and further soil types are included in Key 2. The main horizons used below are described in the Introduction (p. 1). Key 2 can be used independently from, or subsequent to, Key 1. A summary of diagnostic horizons is presented in Fig. 5.

1. Does the soil have podzolic B horizon features (Bf, Bs, Bh)?

   These are iron pans or red/reddish/red-brown/blackish horizons (distinct layers, not just blotches or mottles) in the lower half of a mineral soil (Ef, Bs or Bh horizons, see Fig. 4 and note below).

   Yes .... **Podzol** (Key 1.1, opposite)

   No 2

2. Is the B Horizon gleyed (Bg)?

   This is a red or reddish mottling in the grey or brown background colour. It can also be a uniform grey with faint/sparse/no mottling to the base of the profile.

   Yes .... **Gley Soil** (Key 1.2, opposite)

   No 3

3. Does the soil have a thick accumulation (more than 10 cm in depth) of organic matter – other than roots (O horizon) – over the soil mineral material or bedrock; or a thinner humus horizon directly over bedrock or mineral matter? i.e. no A horizon present.

   An O horizon consists predominantly of organic matter, often peaty, with recognisable plant remains, or of decayed humus, with little mineral matter; blackish or brownish in colour.

   Yes .... **Organic Soil** (Key 1.3, p. 14)

   No .... **Brown Earths or other soil** (Key 1.4, p. 14)

Note. Podzolic B horizons (see also Fig. 4).

Bf – A thin iron pan, less than 10 mm thick; brittle or cemented so that it resists force when struck with a solid object such as a hammer, trowel or spade; blackish-reddish brown. See Plate 4.

Bh – An organic rich horizon present in the mineral matter, composed of humus washed down from above, usually with paler coloured horizon above. May be cemented but yields to force when dug; wider and more diffuse than a Bf. See Plate 5.

Bs – A much broader horizon, with diffuse reddish colour.

Key 1.1. Simple Key to Podzols

1. Ea present above a podzolic horizon (see Fig. 3; Plates 4 and 5) 2

- Ea absent (some bleached sand grains may be present) .... *BROWN PODZOLIC SOILS*

  Diffuse reddish Bs horizon present; other podzolic features weakly developed or absent – No Ea (possibly a few bleached sand grains), no Bfe, No Bh. No peaty topsoil but a dark brown A horizon may be present.
  Similar soils: BROWN EARTH; PODZOL

2. Gleying (Fig. 2) present at some position in the profile. Bh sometimes absent 3

- Gleying not present. Bh present (see Fig. 4 and Plate 5) .... *PODZOL*

  Ea horizon present, prominent Bh; No thin **iron** pan or any gleying; Bs horizon may be present below.
  Similar soil: BROWN PODZOLIC

3. Gleying in Ea (Eag), O (Fig. 1) usually present .... *STAGNOPODZOL*

  Peaty topsoil. Gleying present above or within the podzolic B horizon; gleyed Ea (Eag) present over a thin iron pan (Bf). Bs may be present below. 'Stagno-' implies association with stagnant water.
  Similar soils: GLEY PODZOL; STAGNOHUMIC GLEY

- Gleying in lower profile (Bg), Bh present .... *GLEY PODZOL*

  Peaty topsoil may be present. Gleying present below the podzolic B horizon; Ea, Bh present, but no thin iron pan (Bf).
  Similar soils: GLEY PODZOL, STAGNOHUMIC GLEY

Key 1.2. Simple Key to Gleys

1. Thick (c. 10 cm) peaty topsoil .... *STAGNOHUMIC GLEY*

  Gley soils with a peaty topsoil. 'Stagno-' implies stagnant water.
  Similar soils: STAGNOPODZOL; GLEY PODZOL

- No thick accumulation of peaty topsoil 2

2. Dominantly grey coloured, mottling often present .... *STAGNOGLEY*

  Gley soils without a peaty topsoil. Not brown coloured.

- Dominantly brown coloured, mottling present .... *GLEYIC BROWN EARTH*

  Brown soil with gley features-mottling present.
  Similar soil: BROWN EARTH

Key 1.3. Simple Key to Organic Soils

1. Organic accumulation not directly over bedrock (or if so, more than 30 cm deep) ....
.... *PEAT SOIL*

   Deep accumulations of decomposing organic matter.

   Similar soil: RANKER

\- Organic accumulations over bedrock or fragmented rock/mineral matter 2

2. Acid organic matter over bedrock (soil does not fizz with 10% HCl – see Note 1 below),
   humus usually coarse and fibrous (not including roots) .... *RANKER*

   Acidic, fibrous (ignoring active organic matter) directly over bedrock.

   Similar soils: PEAT, RENDZINA

\- Well decomposed humus, usually over limestone or limestone fragments. The soil
   fizzes with 10% HCl (see Note 1 below) at least somewhere in the profile ... *RENDZINA*
                                                                              See Note 2 below

   Thin, organic limestone soils.

   Similar soil: RANKER

Notes.
1. Note that dolomitic limestone will not fizz with cold HCl.
2. Organic matter has accumulated through the formation of stable calcium humates, rather than because of cold,
wetness or acidity. Some mineral matter may be present.

Key 1.4. Brown Earths and Other Soils

These soils are undifferentiated by podzolic B horizons, gleying or thick organic
accumulations. They include the younger soils, not yet fully developed and also the more
uniform BROWN SOILS which possess few characteristic features

1. Well developed mixed mineral-organic A horizon present (Fig. 1) ..... BROWN SOIL ... 2

\- Well developed A horizon absent .... RAW SOIL ... 3

2. A horizon present. Brown B horizon. Does not fizz with 10% HCl* .... *BROWN EARTH*

   Horizon boundaries often poorly defined. A, B, C present; A well developed, no Ea, Bf, Bs or Bh.

   Similar soil: GLEYIC BROWN EARTH

\- As above, but on calcareous material. B horizon fizzes with 10% HCl* ....
   .... *BROWN CALCAREOUS EARTH*

   Soil undifferentiated by strong horizontal zonation. No Ea, Bf, Bs or Bh. Calcareous.

   Similar soil: BROWN EARTH

   *Note that dolomitic limestone will not fizz with cold HCl.

3. Read three alternatives

- On fine-grained alluvium .... *RAW ALLUVIAL SOIL*
  Horizons not well developed. Often near estuaries or in river basins.

- On sand .... *RAW SAND*
  Horizons not well developed. Sand dune soils.

- On fractured bedrock material (e.g. scree) .... *RAW SKELETAL SOIL*
  Horizons not well developed. On screes and other fractured rock.

KEY 2. DETAILED SOILS KEYS

1. Podzolic B horizons present (Bf, Bh, Bs) (see Fig. 4) .... **KEY 2.1** ... *PODZOLIC SOILS*
   (below)

- Podzolic B horizons absent 2

2. Gleying present (see Introduction, p. 1, and Fig. 2) .... **KEY 2.2** ... *GLEYED SOILS*
   (p. 16)

- Gleying absent 3

3. Thick (more than 10 cm in depth) organic surface layer (see Introduction, p. 1, and Fig. 1) .... **KEY 2.3** ... *ORGANIC SOILS* (p. 20)

- Organic surface layer less than 10 cm in depth **KEY 2.4** ....
  .... *BROWN SOILS and OTHER SOILS* (p. 22)

Key 2.1. Podzolic Soils

1. Ea present. Bs present or absent 2

- Ea absent. Bs present .... BROWN PODZOLIC SOIL 4

2. Gleying present at some position in the profile 3

- Gleying absent .... PODZOL 5

3. Gleying in Ea (Eag). O usually present (above Bh if present) .... STAGNOPODZOL 7

- Gleying lower in profile (Bg). Bh present .... GLEY PODZOL 9

4. Humose A horizon; blackish .... *HUMIC BROWN PODZOLIC SOIL*

- A horizon not humose; brownish .... *TYPICAL BROWN PODZOLIC SOIL*

5. Bs present 6

- Bs absent .... *HUMUS PODZOL*

6. Bh greater than 2.5 cm .... *HUMO-FERRIC PODZOL*

- Bh less than 2.5 cm or absent .... *FERRIC PODZOL*

7. Bf present, Bs absent 8

- Bf absent, Bs present .... *FERRIC STAGNOPODZOL*

8. Bh more than 2.5 cm thick .... *HUMUS-IRON PAN STAGNOPODZOL*

- Bh less than 2.5 cm thick, or absent .... *IRON PAN STAGNOPODZOL*

9 Impermeable layer (usually clay) at the base of the profile .... *STAGNOGLEY PODZOL*

- Coarse sandy or loamy texture; low-lying sites 10

10. Bs present .... *HUMO-FERRIC GLEY-PODZOL*

-    Bs absent .... *TYPICAL GLEY-PODZOL*

Key 2.2. Gleyed Soils

1. Lacking a distinct topsoil, found on intertidal flats and salt marshes .... *RAW GLEY SOIL*

- Has a distinct topsoil, not on intertidal flats or salt marshes 2

2. A dominantly organic soil, shallow – with bedrock or skeletal material (more than 35% volume stones) within 30 cm, calcareous or non-calcareous .... GLEYED ORGANIC SOIL ... **KEY 2.3** (p. 20)

- Not as above 3

3. Dominantly brown-red in colour (Munsell hue 10YR or redder) ....
.... GLEYED BROWN SOIL, **KEY 2.4** (p. 22)

- Paler dominant colours, usually grey (with strong or weak red mottles) 4

4. Clayey texture at surface (or within 30 cm of the surface), smooth-faced blocky or prismatic beds, often cracked when dry, gleying often weak and starting below 40 cm
.... PELOSOL ... **KEY 2.4** (p. 22)

- Not as above, or if as above *then* gleying is present within 40 cm of the surface ....
.... GLEY SOIL 5

5. A low-lying site with flat topography .... GROUND-WATER GLEY SOIL 6

- High site > 3 m O.D. .... SURFACE-WATER GLEY SOIL 24

6. Sandy texture, no argillic horizon 7

- Texture not sandy or, if so, soil with an argillic horizon 10

7. Humose or peaty topsoil present .... HUMIC-SANDY GLEY SOIL 8

- Humose or peaty topsoil absent .... SANDY-GLEY SOIL 9

8. Calcareous within the top 40 cm and below ....
.... CALCAREOUS HUMIC-SANDY GLEY SOIL

- Not calcareous within the top 40 cm .... TYPICAL HUMIC-SANDY GLEY SOIL

9. Calcareous within the top 40 cm .... CALCAREOUS SANDY-GLEY SOIL

- Not calcareous within the top 40 cm .... TYPICAL SANDY-GLEY SOIL

10. Humose or peaty topsoil 11

- Topsoil neither humose nor peaty 15

11. On recent alluvium .... HUMIC-ALLUVIAL GLEY SOIL 12

- Not in recent alluvium .... HUMIC GLEY SOIL 13

12. Calcareous within 40 cm of the surface, and below ....
.... *CALCAREOUS HUMIC-ALLUVIAL GLEY SOIL*

-   Not calcareous within the top 40 cm .... *TYPICAL HUMIC-ALLUVIAL GLEY SOIL*

13. Clay-enriched subsoil present .... *ARGILLIC HUMIC GLEY SOIL*

-   Clay-enriched subsoil absent 14

14. Calcareous within 80 cm of the surface, and below ....
.... *CALCAREOUS HUMIC GLEY SOIL*

-   Not calcareous in the top 80 cm .... *TYPICAL HUMIC GLEY SOIL*

15. In recent alluvium .... ALLUVIAL GLEY SOIL 16

-   Not in recent alluvium 20

16. Calcareous within 40 cm of the surface, and below 17

-   Not calcareous within the top 40 cm 18

17. Clayey texture at the surface or within 30 cm of the surface, smooth-faced blocky or prismatic beds, often cracked when dry (Pelofeatures) ....
.... *PELO-CALCAREOUS ALLUVIAL GLEY SOIL*

-   Pelofeatures absent .... *CALCAREOUS ALLUVIAL GLEY SOIL*

18. Clayey texture at the surface or within 30 cm of the surface, smooth-faced blocky or prismatic beds, often cracked when dry (Pelofeatures) ... *PELO-ALLUVIAL GLEY SOIL*

-   Pelofeatures absent 19

19. Evidence of sulphide oxidation to form highly acidic soil, pH less than 4, yellow mottles (hue 2.5 or yellower) and chroma of 6 or more, within 80 cm of the surface ....
.... *SULPHURIC ALLUVIAL GLEY SOIL*

-   Not as above .... *ALLUVIAL GLEY SOIL*

20. Clay-enriched subsoil .... ARGILLIC GLEY SOIL 21

- No clay-enriched subsoil .... CAMBIC GLEY SOIL 22

21. Sandy layer more than 15 cm thick .... *SANDY ARGILLIC GLEY SOIL*

- Any sandy layer 15 cm, or less, thick .... *TYPICAL ARGILLIC GLEY SOIL*

22. Calcareous within 40 cm of the surface .... *CALCAREOUS CAMBIC GLEY SOIL*

- Not calcareous within 40 cm of the surface 23

23. Clayey texture at the surface or within 30 cm of the surface, smooth-faced blocky or prismatic beds, often cracked when dry (Pelofeatures) ..... *PELO-CAMBIC GLEY SOILS*

- Pelofeatures absent .... *TYPICAL CAMBIC GLEY SOILS*

24. Humose or peaty topsoil present .... STAGNOHUMIC GLEY SOILS 25

- Topsoil neither humose nor peaty .... STAGNOGLEY SOILS 27

25. Clay-enriched subsoil 26

- Subsoil not clay-enriched .... *CAMBIC STAGNOHUMIC GLEY SOIL*

26. Reddish or reddish mottled .... *PALAEO-ARGILLIC STAGNOHUMIC GLEY SOIL*

- Not as above .... *ARGILLIC STAGNOHUMIC GLEY SOIL*

27. Clayey texture at the surface or within 30 cm of the surface, smooth-faced blocky or prismatic beds, often cracked when dry (Pelofeatures) .... *PELO-STAGNOGLEY SOIL*

- Pelo-features absent 28

28. Clay-enriched subsoil present .... *TYPICAL STAGNOGLEY SOIL*

- Clay-enriched subsoil absent .... *CAMBIC STAGNOGLEY SOIL*

Key 2.3. Organic Soils

1. Not over bedrock or skeletal material, or if so, then the bedrock or skeletal material is more than 30 cm below the surface .... PEAT SOILS 2

- Over bedrock or skeletal material; with a total depth of less than 30 cm ....
.... LITHOMORPHIC SOILS 5

2. Undrained raw peat, wet to 20 cm below the surface 3

- Earthy, drained sites 4

3. Recognisable plant remains .... *RAW FIBROUS PEAT SOIL*

- Plant remains unrecognisable .... *RAW AMORPHOUS PEAT SOIL*

4. Recognisable plant remains .... *EARTHY FIBROUS PEAT SOIL*

- Plant remains unrecognisable .... *EARTHY AMORPHOUS PEAT SOIL*

5. Calcareous or at least partly calcareous, soil. Humose topsoil, plant remains usually not recognisable .... RENDZINA 10

- Non-calcareous soil (may be over calcareous rock, but the soil is non-calcareous) ....
.... RANKER 6

6. On bedrock or skeletal material .... RANKER 7

- On sand .... *SAND RANKER*

7. E horizon present .... *PODZOLIC RANKER*

- E horizon absent 8

8. Gleying present .... *GLEYIC RANKER*

- Gleying absent 9

9. Humose or peaty topsoil .... *HUMIC RANKER*

- Topsoil neither humose nor peaty .... *BROWN RANKER*

10. On sandy material .... *SAND-PARARENDZINA*

- Not on sand 11

11. On chalk or limestone .... RENDZINA 15

- Not on chalk or limestone 12

12. Calcareous rock (e.g. mudstone, sandstone) .... *PARARENDZINA*

- Calcareous alluvium, lake marl or tufa .... RENDZINA-LIKE ALLUVIAL SOIL 13

13. Gleyed 14

- Not gleyed .... *TYPICAL RENDZINA-LIKE ALLUVIAL SOIL*

14. Humose or peaty topsoil .... *HUMIC GLEYIC RENDZINA-LIKE ALLUVIAL SOIL*

- Without humose or peaty topsoil .... *GLEYIC RENDZINA-LIKE ALLUVIAL SOIL*

15. Gleyed 16

- Not gleyed 17

16. Humose or peaty topsoil .... *HUMIC GLEYIC RENDZINA*

- Topsoil neither humose nor peaty .... *GLEYIC RENDZINA*

17. Humose topsoil .... *HUMIC RENDZINA*

- Topsoil not humose 18

18. Developed on recent colluvium .... *COLLUVIAL RENDZINA*

- Not developed on recent colluvium 19

19. Distinct brownish-coloured topsoil .... *BROWN RENDZINA*

- Distinct greyish-coloured topsoil .... *GREY RENDZINA*

KEY 2.4. Brown Soils and Other Soils

1. Clayey texture at the surface (or within 30 cm of the surface), smooth-faced blocky or prismatic beds, often cracked when dry .... PELOSOL 2

- Not as above 4

2. Clay-enriched subsurface horizon present .... *ARGILLIC PELOSOL*

- No clay-enriched subsoil 3

3. Calcareous .... *CALCAREOUS PELOSOL*

- Not calcareous .... *NON-CALCAREOUS PELOSOL*

4. Dominantly brown or reddish brown colour, with subsurface horizons (e.g. B, C) usually fawn/brown/reddish brown in colour .... BROWN SOIL 5

- No subsurface horizon visible .... RAW SOIL 31

5. Calcareous subsurface horizon present 6

- Not calcareous in profile 13

6. On sand or alluvium 7

- Not on sand or alluvium .... BROWN CALCAREOUS EARTH 10

7. On sand .... BROWN CALCAREOUS SAND 8

- On alluvium .... BROWN CALCAREOUS ALLUVIAL SOIL 9

8. With gleying .... *GLEYIC BROWN CALCAREOUS SAND*

- Without gleying .... *TYPICAL BROWN CALCAREOUS SAND*

9. With gleying .... *GLEYIC BROWN CALCAREOUS ALLUVIAL SOIL*

- Without gleying .... *TYPICAL BROWN CALCAREOUS ALLUVIAL SOIL*

10. Gleying present 11

-   Gleying absent 12

11. Slowly permeable subsurface horizon present ....
    .... *STAGNOGLEYIC BROWN CALCAREOUS EARTH*

-   Not as above .... *GLEYIC BROWN CALCAREOUS EARTH*

12. On recent colluvium .... *COLLUVIAL BROWN CALCAREOUS EARTH*

-   On other substrata .... *TYPICAL BROWN CALCAREOUS EARTH*

13. On sand or alluvium 14

-   Not on sand or alluvium 15

14. On sand .... BROWN SAND 16

-   On alluvium .... BROWN ALLUVIAL SOIL 20

15. Clay-enriched subsoil present .... ARGILLIC BROWN EARTH 21

-   No clay-enriched subsoil .... BROWN EARTH 26

16. With gleying 17

-   Without gleying 19

17. Slowly permeable subsurface horizon present .... *STAGNOGLEYIC BROWN SAND*

-   Without slowly permeable subsurface horizon 18

18. Clay-enriched subsurface horizon present .... *GLEYIC ARGILLIC BROWN SAND*

-   Without a clay-enriched subsurface horizon .... *GLEYIC BROWN SAND*

19. Clay-enriched subsurface horizon present .... *ARGILLIC BROWN EARTH*

-   Without a clay-enriched subsurface horizon .... *TYPICAL BROWN SAND*

20. Gleying present .... *GLEYIC BROWN ALLUVIAL SOIL*

-   Gleying absent .... *TYPICAL BROWN ALLUVIAL SOIL*

21. Reddish or reddish mottled .... PALAEO-ARGILLIC BROWN EARTH 22

-   Not reddish, or reddish mottled 24

22. Gleying present 23

-   Gleying absent .... *TYPICAL PALAEO-ARGILLIC BROWN EARTH*

23. Slowly permeable subsurface horizon present ....
    .... *STAGNOGLEY PALAEO-ARGILLIC BROWN EARTH*

-   Without slowly permeable subsurface horizon ....
    .... *GLEYIC PALAEO-ARGILLIC BROWN EARTH*

24. Gleying present 25

-   Gleying absent .... *TYPICAL ARGILLIC BROWN EARTH*

25. Slowly permeable subsurface horizon present ....
    .... *STAGNOGLEYIC ARGILLIC BROWN EARTH*

-   Without slowly permeable subsurface horizon ..... *GLEYIC ARGILLIC BROWN EARTH*

26. Gleying present 27

-   Gleying absent 30

27. Ferruginous weathered B horizon present 28

-   Without a ferruginous weathered B horizon 29

28. Slowly permeable subsurface horizon present ....
    .... *STAGNOGLEYIC FERRITIC BROWN EARTH*

-   Without slowly permeable subsurface horizon ..... *GLEYIC FERRITIC BROWN EARTH*

29. Slowly permeable subsurface horizon present .... *STAGNOGLEYIC BROWN EARTH*

-    Without slowly permeable subsurface horizon .... *GLEYIC BROWN EARTH*

30. Ferruginous weathered B horizon present .... *FERRITIC BROWN EARTH*

-    Without ferruginous weathered B horizon .... *TYPICAL BROWN EARTH*

31. On sand .... *RAW SAND*

-    Not on sand 32

32. Fine-grained material 33

-    Coarse-grained material .... *RAW SKELETAL SOIL*

33. On alluvium .... *RAW ALLUVIAL SOIL*

-    On other loamy or clayey material .... *RAW EARTH*

APPENDIX 1
DISCUSSION NOTES FOR TEACHERS ON THE FIELD TEACHING OF SOILS

This is a personal view, arising from experience with many sixth-form groups and their teachers.

While the production of this key is intended to assist with the field identification of soils, it should be stressed that it is more important, in an educational context, to understand the processes operating within a soil. Something useful can be gained from the inspection of any soil type. The questions which should be asked initially involve (1) organic matter, (2) aeration and (3) leaching – as stressed in the Introduction. The depth of organic matter can be linked readily with cycling efficiency, wetness, temperature and acidity by working backwards using Fig. 6. That is to say, deep accumulations of organic matter mean that conditions are of high acidity and/or coldness and/or wetness and/or result from a lack of cycling, (and vice versa). Thin accumulations of organic matter and browner A horizons indicate efficient decay processes, rapid recycling and the incorporation of organic matter into the mineral matter (except on sites where organic matter is obviously sparse for other reasons – waste tips, etc.). Red and grey colours can be used to indicate the oxidation status. Leaching processes can be deduced from accumulations lower down in the soil profile and they can also be predicted to occur from accumulations of organic matter on the top of the profile because these act as sources of organic acids.

These relatively simple factors should be discussed initially and they can be applied as first principles to any soil – before there is any concern about type. Many soils, seen in a pit section, do not conform to ideal types, let alone to those portrayed in A-level and undergraduate textbooks. This often leads to confusion, perplexity and disenchantment for students and teachers alike. But, however problematical it may sometimes appear to identify and classify soils, the principles of organic cycling, aeration and leaching can be applied to virtually all soils encountered in the United Kingdom, unless there has been some disturbance. Slope movement and deep ploughing, for example, can cause confusion as they may lead to stone layers being present in organic horizons or to podzols having uniform A horizons above an iron-rich layer, with no Ea or O horizon.

Another point of confusion can arise with grey coloured horizons as these may be formed either (a) because iron has been leached out (Ea horizons) or (b) because iron is present, but in a reduced form (gleyed horizons). The Keys have, therefore, been constructed to minimise this problem and also to deal with problems due to O horizons, which may occur both in podzolic and gley soils. Firstly, Key 1 depends on the identification of a podzolic B horizon (Bfe, Bh, Bs) as the unique, diagnostic feature of a podzol. Ea and O horizons are often present but Ea may be confused with gley horizons and O is present in other soils, as discussed above. Therefore, the podzolic B horizon is used to differentiate podzols from other soils (Fig. 6). In practice, podzolic B horizons can be difficult to distinguish/identify but a Bfe is a clearly visible, thin (1-2 mm), often wavy, coherent and cemented layer (dark reddish, brownish or blackish in colour), usually resisting force when struck (often looking like a rusty steel sheet buried in the soil), a Bh is identifiable as humus which forms an obvious layer within the mineral matter; a Bs is a diffuse reddish colour. The latter may be problematical in Southwest England and other areas

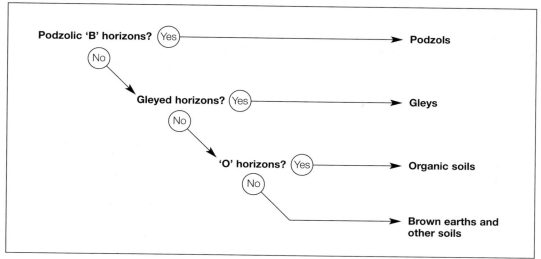

Figure 6. Simplified introductory key to soil types (see also Key 1, p. 12).

where Triassic desert weathering processes have given the whole soil a reddish tinge, but the redness should be in the lower part of the profile and if a Munsell colour chart is available (see Glossary) colours redder than 5YR and mostly 2.5 YR are present – i.e. a red-brown, ochreous colour (similar to the 'copper' in the 'Crown plus two' colour catalogue, gloss paint section), whether or not a pale leached horizon is clearly evident above. Brown earths have colours 7.5YR to 10YR. If these podzolic B horizons are absent then move down the key – and only then are grey colours considered. If present (with or without red mottling) they indicate gleying and this key sequence minimises confusion of Ea with Bg horizons because Ea is not initially seen as diagnostic. Similarly, O horizons, while they may be present in podzols and gleys, are only seen as diagnostic when podzols and gleys have been eliminated by the absence of podzolic B horizons and gley horizons in turn. This avoids confusion with podzol and gley O horizons. Finally, only those soils distinguished by the absence of podzolic B horizons, gleyed horizons and O horizons are left and these are the brown earths together with some alluvial soils. Brown earths are vertically not very differentiated and have weak, indistinct horizons.

Such an approach combines the initial discussion of processes (organic matter, aeration and leaching) with identification so that classification naturally leads on from the discussion of processes. It broadly classifies soils, which is all that may be possible in a short field visit. It helps to maintain interest because it avoids a welter of classificatory terms and there is no over-riding stress of the initial need (panic?) to classify the soil. It focuses on the all important processes but provides the interest of a broad label of a soil type. It also focuses on the visible evidence of genesis rather than any preconceived assumption. Such an approach is simplistic but practical in a short period, especially if initial interest is limited. Once the seed of interest has been planted and the satisfaction of understanding the basic principles and types established, it is then possible to proceed to the finer points in Key 2 if desired. This process is over-simplified, and aimed at gaining interest and mastery of the basics, but it is, in fact, reasonably faithful to a more detailed soil survey approach – which many find off-putting if it is introduced at the first step. Thus, Key 1 can be used before Key 2 and then further information may also be found in Avery (1980) for more detailed studies. Reference to the extremely useful article by Burnham (1980) may also be made after Key 1 has been used.

So many teachers have stressed that they find soils field teaching difficult that I feel that it is apposite to provide a simple approach, as in Key 1 (and Fig. 6), which is reasonably faithful to a more detailed approach and which has been found to be effective with teachers of limited soils background and with students whose motivation is limited. I shall be interested to hear of teaching experiences using this approach and I hope that it will help to bridge the gap between the search for an 'ideal A-level podzol' and a more detailed approach which can be initially less rewarding. Appendix 2 includes aspects of soil profile description which can be considered once the basic processes and types have been established.

APPENDIX 2
SOIL PROFILE DESCRIPTION AND HAND TEXTURING KEY

A full soil profile description can be undertaken if desired (Courtney & Trudgill, 1984, Chapter 6), but, as with soil identification, focusing on one or two observations is often more worthwhile at an initial stage; more detailed descriptions can follow once some basic essentials have been dealt with. *Soil texture* is of primary importance, and is used as a diagnostic character in the keys. A chart for the identification of soil texture is given opposite.

Soil texture

Sand gives structure to the soil. A sandy soil is not prone to compaction but may be easily eroded by running water. Clays are important in soils as they hold many plant nutrients (see Courtney & Trudgill, 1984, p. 16 and pp. 27-30). Clay soils are cohesive and, therefore, not generally prone to erosion but they can be impermeable – unless well structured – and 'heavy' when cultivated. Silts are often prone to compaction and can be eroded by the wind. An ideal soil, for agriculture etc., is a loam, combining the strength of sand and the nutrient-holding properties of clay, together with silt.

Rooting depth

The distribution of roots can be instructive in relation to such factors as plant nutrition and water-logging. For instance, fine, feeder roots may be concentrated under the layers of decomposing organic matter where nutrients are being released by decay processes. Observation of roots growing only to mid-profile depth suggest poor drainage at the base of the profile, resulting in water-logging and low oxygen conditions limiting root extension or leading to die-back of roots in the wetter, winter months.

Consistency

As explained in the Glossary, there are several terms which can be used to describe the firmness or looseness of the soil (and see also Courtriey & Trudgill, 1984, p. 98). The basic interest lies in how well-cemented a soil is (e.g. by iron oxides or organic matter in podzols), giving a hard, firm or brittle consistency. Soils with a soft consistency can be prone to compaction under cultivation.

Colour

Of basic importance is the presence of oxidised iron (red, reddish, red-yellow, red-orange colours) and humus (black, blackish, dark brown colours) which help with identification of soil processes and types. These can be described in general terms or by using the Munsell Colour Scheme outlined in the Glossary (and Courtney & Trudgill, 1984, pp. 94 and 95).

These characteristics can be described for each horizon or selectively for the main soil B Horizon, as time allows.

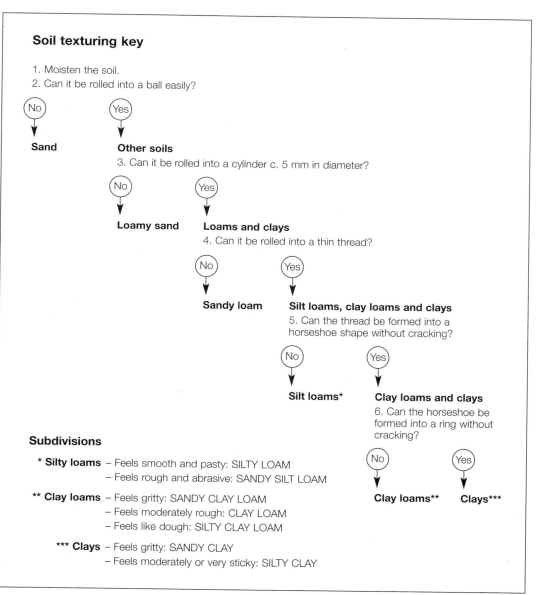

Figure 7. Soil texture key.

Structure and porosity

Structure can be recognised as platey, crumbly, granular or columnar (vertical) (Courtney & Trudgill, 1984, p. 68), but the basic interest is in the pore spaces left between for penetration of air and water. Study the profile and consider how easily water and air can move through the soil, allowing drainage of excess water and the penetration of oxygen to plant roots.

APPENDIX 3
SOIL HORIZON BOOKING FORM

Measure and describe each layer visible in your soil pit and then use the *Key to soil horizon* to identify them.

Layer	cm	Description	Horizon name
1			
2			
3			
4			
5			
6			
7			
8			
9			
10			

GLOSSARY

(Capitals in the text indicate a cross reference to another entry)

A HORIZON. Mixed mineral-organic matter at or near the soil surface, TOPSOIL.

AERATION. Refers to the presence of atmospheric oxygen in the soil, usually in the absence of waterlogging (see also OXIDATION).

ALLUVIAL. Fine grained-material (silts, clays) deposited by rivers or in estuaries (see Avery, 1980, p. 35).

AMORPHOUS. No visible structure – in HUMUS and PEATS, no plant remains recognizable; well decomposed.

ARGILLIC. CLAY-rich. If referring to a soil HORIZON, contains more CLAY than the overlying horizon (see Appendix 1 for hand TEXTURING). Refer to Avery (1980) p. 30 for a more detailed definition of an argillic B Horizon.

B HORIZON. A dominantly mineral HORIZON weathered or altered in some way; normally underlies the surface A HORIZON (see Avery, 1980, pp. 17-18).

Bh HORIZON. A PODZOLIC B HORIZON of dark-coloured (brownish or blackish) down washed HUMUS, often in the form of humus coatings around mineral grains (and, therefore, distinguishable from buried A horizons). May be cemented but yields to force when dug; more diffuse than a Ef (below). See Avery (1980), pp. 18-19).

Bf HORIZON. A PODZOLIC B HORIZON: a thin IRON FAN less than 10 mm thick, brittle or cemented so that it resists force when struck with a solid object such as a trowel, hammer or spade; reddish-brown-blackish, looking like rusty sheet steel and sharply defined. (See Avery, 1980, p. 18).

Bg HORIZON. A GLEYED, B HORIZON, dominantly grey in colour with or without prominent red/reddish MOTTLES on PED faces and/or root channels. (See Avery, 1980, p. 18).

Bs HORIZON. A diffuse, reddish coloured PODZOLIC B HORIZON, colours redder than 2.5-5.OYR (see MUNSELL COLOUR) formed by downwashed iron Gmd/or weathering *in situ*. (See Avery, 1980, p. 19).

BROWN EARTH/BROWN SOIL. Defined here as a soil not distinguishable by prominent PODZOLISATION, GLEYING or organic accumulations. A soil of weak horizon definition, but usually with an A, B, C sequence. See Avery (1980) pp. 45-49 for a more detailed definition.

CALCAREOUS. Having calcium carbonate present so that the soil reacts by fizzing in 10% hydrochloric acid (note: dolomite only fizzes with warm HCl; dolomitic soils can be classed as calcareous, so if warm HCl is not available a geology map will be an asset for predicting the occurrence of calcareous soils).

CAMBIC. Cambic is a term applied to GLEY soils which are LOAMY or CLAYEY, with no significant CLAY enriched subsoil (i.e. non-ARGILLIC).

CATION. A positively-charged ion.

CHELATXON. The incorporation of a METAL cation (in soils, usually iron and/or aluminium, but also calcium, magnesium, sodium or potassium) within the chemical structure of an organic compound, usually an organic acid derived from the decay of HUMUS; the iron or other cation can thus be moved down the profile if the organic matter is downwashed – this process is termed cheluvation or PODZOLISATION. (See also Courtney & Trudgill, 1984, p. 9 and 36.)

CHROMA. See under MUNSELL COLOUR.

CLAY. Very fine particles, less than 0.002 mm in diameter (see Courtney & Trudgill, 1984, p. 13). A clay soil can be moulded into shapes and rolled into a thread and ring without breaking up (see Appendix 1).

COLLUVIUM. A slope-foot deposit, usually fine-grained SILT or CLAY but may be SANDY or with small stones, formed by slope-wash and creep processes, often more active in the past than the present, i.e. under post-glacial conditions before the establishment of a vegetation cover. Differentiated from scree and SKELETAL material as these include larger angular fragments.

COLOUR. See MUNSELL COLOUR.

CONSISTENCE. This is a term used to describe the degree and kind of cohesion of soil material and can be: *loose,* falls apart easily; *friable,* crumbles under gentle pressure; *firm,* offers resistance; *hard; brittle; plastic; sticky* or *soft* (see Courtney & Trudgill, 1984, p. 98 for further definitions).

Ea HORIZON. A bleached whitish or greyish horizon, usually underlying an organic horizon, from which iron has been LEACHED by CHELATION, normally overlying a PODZOLIC B HORIZON (see Avery, 1980, p. 28 – 'albic E Horizon').

ELUVIAL. A term applied to HORIZONS depleted of soluble/mobile constituents by LEACHING. Usually paler in colour than HORIZONS above or below.

F HORIZON. Organic layer under L HORIZON; plant remains only partly recognisable.

FERRIC IRON. Iron in the OXIDISED form, IRON III compounds, usually reddish in colour; i.e. 'rusty' iron (see Courtney & Trudgill, 1984, p. 9). See also Bg HORIZON.

FERRITIC A HORIZON with a noticeable amount of reddish oxidised iron (FERRIC IRON) (see Courtney & Trudgill, 1984, p. 104).

FERROUS IRON. Iron in the reduced form, IRON II compounds, usually pale grey/bluey-grey in colour (see Courtney & Trudgill, 1980, p. 104).

FERRUGINOUS. Having a high proportion of OXIDISED or FERRIC IRON. Red or red-black in colour, often with the iron in coatings on grains or nodules.

FIBROUS. Refers to ORGANIC matter or PEAT where the plant remains are still recognisable (as opposed to AMORPHOUS).

GLEYING. Soil-forming processes in waterlogged soils where the REDUCING conditions are prevalent, and iron is present in the FERROUS form, giving a predominantly grey or blue-grey colour, with or without red MOTTLES of oxidised F horizon. Organic layer under L HORIZON; plant remains only partly recognisable.

GROUNDWATER GLEY. A gley soil formed in low-lying situations with poor drainage and flat topography, less than 3 m O.D.

H HORIZON. Humus layer under F HORIZON; plant remains unrecognisable.

HORIZON. A horizontal layer differentiated in some way from the material above and below it. See Courtney & Trudgill, 1984, p. 92 for definitions of horizon types.

HUE. See MUNSELL COLOUR.

HUMIC. With a high proportion of HUMUS.

HUMOSE HORIZON. An A HORIZON of mixed mineral and organic matter but where humus forms a high proportion, giving a dark, blackish colour.

HUMUS. Decayed organic matter, such as plant remains, which are unrecognisable.

IMPERMEABLE. Not allowing the passage of water.

IRON II Iron in FERRIC form, OXIDISED iron.

IRON III Iron in the FERROUS form, REDUCED iron

IRON PAN. Alternative name for a Bf HORIZON.

L HORIZON. Surface leaf litter layer; plant remains recognisable

LEACHING. The downwashing of soluble or otherwise mobile material through the soil (see Courtney & Trudgill, 1984, p. 7).

LITHOMORPHIC. Soils with a little altered mineral substratum. (Rock or SKELETAL material) starting at or within a 40 cm depth, usually with a HUMOSE or PEATY topsoil; includes RANKERS, and RENDZINA soils.

LOAM. A mixture of SAND, SILT and CLAY, see Courtney & Trudgill, 1980, p. 16.

MOTTLING. Sporadic coloured patches, usually of redder FERRIC IRON in a greyer background colour in GLEY soils.

METAL. A substance which yields CATIONS on dissociation in water.

MUNSELL COLOUR. A system for the description of soil colour, described in detail by Courtney & Trudgill, 1984, pp. 94-95, whereby colour is described by: HUE, the dominant spectral colour (red, yellow, etc.); VALUE, referring to lightness or blackness (0-10) and CHROMA, referring to purity or saturation of the colour. The colours are reported in the order Hue, Value/Chroma, with Hue sub-divided four times (2.5, 5, 7.5 and 10).

O HORIZON. A dominantly organic peaty horizon. Can be further divided, into L, F and H HORIZONS. Described in further detail by Avery, 1980, p. 25.

OCHREOUS. A reddish horizon dominated by FERRIC IRON and distinguished by its colour (red, reddish, red-orange, red-yellow).

ORGANIC SOIL. A soil with more than 30 cm organic matter; PEAT SOILS.

OXIDATION. Loss of a negative electron, usually under oxygen-rich conditions but also under alkaline conditions, transforming FERROUS IRON (IRON II) to FERRIC IRON (IRON III). See Trudgill, 1983, p. 72-73. The oxygen may be present in air in the soil, or dissolved in soil water.

PALAEO-ARGILLIC HORIZON. A reddish B HORIZON, enriched in clay and formed by weathering in conditions prior to the last glaciations (see Avery, 1980, pp. 30 and 31 for detailed definitions).

PEAT SOIL. Soil with more than 30 cm organic matter present at the surface (see Avery, 1980, p. 59).

PED. A unit of soil structure into which the soil breaks down when handled (or when dried out). See Courtney & Trudgill, 1984, pp. 17 and 18, 67-71.

PELOFEATURES. Dominantly clayey texture at the surface or within 30 cm of the surface, smooth-faced or prismatic PEDS (vertical structures) often cracked when dry, GLEYING may be present but often weak. See also Avery, 1980, p. 35.

PELOSOL. A soil having PELOFEATURES.

PODZOL. Soil having a PODZOLIC B HORIZON of downwashed iron and/or humus or iron weathered *in situ* (see Bf HORIZON, Bh HORIZON and Bs HORIZON respectively). Usually with an Ea HORIZON from which iron has been leached by chelation, though this may have been disturbed by cultivation. See Avery, 1980, p. 49.

PODZOLIC B HORIZON. This is a Bf, Bh or Bs HORIZON, produced by LEACHING and CHELATION characteristic of a PODZOL. See Avery, 1980, p. 28.

PODZOLISATION. The downwashing of iron and/or humus through the action of organic acids by CHELATION. See Courtney & Trudgill, 1984, pp. 36-39.

RANKER. These are non-CALCAREOUS, LITHOMORPHIC SOILS usually having bedrock or SKELETAL material within 40 cm of the surface. If lying over limestone, the soil is non-CALCAREOUS.

REDUCTION. Gain of a negative electron under oxygen-poor conditions or under acid conditions; transformation of FERRIC IRON (IRON III) to FERROUS IRON (IRON II). See Trudgill, 1983, pp. 72 and 73.

RENDZINA. A CALCAREOUS, LITHOMORPHIC SOIL with bedrock or SKELETAL material within 30 cm from the surface. See Avery, 1980, p. 43.

SAND. Coarse soil particles, 0.02-2.0 mm in diameter, imparting a gritty feel to the soil. See Appendix 2 and Courtney & Trudgill: 1984, p. 13.

SESQUIOXIDES. Oxides with a ratio of element to oxygen of 1:1.5, e.g. Fe_2O_3, Al_2O_3.

SILT. Particles of size between sand and clay, 0.002-0.02 mm in diameter, imparting a silky or soapy feel to the soil. See Appendix 2 and Courtney & Trudgill, 1984, p. 13.

SKELETAL MATERIAL. Fragments of bedrock produced by mechanical weathering, such as frost action, or by prolonged chemical weathering, leading to the occurrence of stone fragments, often angular in shape, also may be admixtures of sand and smaller stones.

STAGNO-. A prefix for GLEYS and PODZOLS, implying water-logged, *stagnant* water conditions, usually with a subsurface horizon which is only slowly permeable.

STRUCTURE. The arrangement of soil particles into PEDS.

SURFACE WATER GLEY. Gleys occurring at elevations greater than 3 m O.D. due to locally waterlogged conditions and/or impermeable parent material.

TEXTURE. The 'feel' of the soil – see Appendix 2, in relation to particle size distribution. See also SAND, SILT, LOAM, CLAY.

TOPSOIL. General term for the near-surface layers, approximating to the A HORIZON.

TYPICAL. Implying that the soil conforms to the general notion of a soil type and is not differentiated by modifying features.

VALUE. See MUNSELL COLOUR.